Accounting Technician
Pilot Papers - Level A & B

Contents

ACCA ACCOUNTING TECHNICIAN

Introduction to Pilot Papers

From June 1998 we will be offering the examinations for the ACCA's Accounting Technician qualification. As well as completing the examinations, students will have to gain relevant practical training to achieve the Technician qualification.

There are nine examinations, split into three levels, all designed to test the knowledge and understanding needed to work in accounting support roles.

This booklet contains sample questions for Level A and Pilot Papers for Level B:

Level A – Multiple choice questions only, 2 hour exams

A1   Transaction Accounting
A2   Office Practice and Procedure

Level B – 2 hour exams

B1   Maintaining Financial Records and Accounts
B2   Cost Accounting Systems
B3   Information Technology

The purpose of the pilot papers is to give an indication of the style and type of questions to be set and to show the approach to examining at each level.

The suggested answers for Level B presented in this booklet are longer and more detailed than those expected from a student taking the examinations. These answers are intended to provide students with an indication of the form and standard of answer which they should try to provide. The suggested answer may not contain all the points that could correctly be made and students should note that credit will be awarded for valid answers which may not be fully covered in this booklet.

For further information contact:

ACCA Education Department
29 Lincoln's Inn Fields
London WC2A 3EE
Tel: 0171 396 5891
Fax: 0171 396 5880

ACCA Accounting Technician Examination

Level A

Paper 1

Transaction Accounting

MCQ Paper:	
Time allowed	2 hours
Sample Questions Only	

The Association of Chartered Certified Accountants

NOTE: These are Sample Questions

Types of business transactions

1   Kew Ltd has an overdraft of £4,400 at the start of June. The following four transactions occurred during June. Kew allows its customers up to 60 days to pay their invoices.

3 June   Kew sells goods worth £10,000 on credit to a customer who always takes the full credit period.
10 June   Kew pays a supplier £8,000.
20 June   Kew sell goods worth £12,000 for cash and allows a 5% discount.
23 June   Cash is received from a customer who has been in dispute with Kew. The original invoice was for £6,000, but Kew has agreed to accept half the invoice value to settle the dispute.

How much does Kew have in the bank at the end of June?

A   £2,000
B   £2,600
C   £10,800
D   £12,000

Answer

A $-$ 4,400 $-$ 8,000 + 11,400 + 3,000

Types of business documentation

2   Victoria & Co wishes to buy goods from Paddington Ltd. **Which of the following is the most likely flow of documents to complete the purchase?**

A   Purchase order, delivery note, goods received note, cheque requisition, invoice.
B   Purchase order, delivery note, goods received note, invoice, cheque requisition.
C   Goods received note, purchase order, delivery note, invoice, cheque requisition.
D   Purchase order, goods received note, delivery note, cheque requisition, invoice.

Answer

B

Banking system

3   **Which of the following is least likely to be an obligation of a bank towards its customer?**

A   To use a professional level of care and skill.
B   To provide confirmation of the balance on the account at any time at the request of the customer.
C   To provide a statement covering a period showing the transactions which have occurred during that period.
D   To provide a statement detailing the profits the bank has made with the the money the customer has deposited.

Answer

D

Cash handling

4   **Which of the following is *not* an effective security procedure?**

A   A key must be inserted in to the cash register before it will operate. Keys are held by authorised personnel.
B   Cash is counted by a responsible person who works on the cash register.
C   The cash reconciliation should be performed by a responsible person who neither operates the cash register nor counts the cash.
D   Cash should be banked as promptly as possible.

Answer

B

Basic distinction between capital and revenue expenditure

5   Colin is the accountant in a firm which has a large fleet of motor vehicles. He is unsure of the distinction between capital and revenue expenditure. Advise Colin as to which of the following would be classified as revenue rather than capital expenditure.

(i)   Purchase of a new delivery van.
(ii)   Redecorating the transport manager's office.
(iii) Paying the road fund licences for the fleet of vehicles.
(iv) Purchase for a new exhaust for a van.

A   all four expenses
B   (ii), (iii) and (iv)
C   (i) and (ii)
D   (iii) only.

Answer

B   (ii)   and (iv) are repairs and maintenance expenses which should maintain the earning capacity of the business. Such expenditure is revenue expenditure.

(iii)   is a motor expense and forms part of the cost of running a business, again it is a revenue expense.

(i)   is the purchase of a fixed asset and should increase the earnings capacity of the business. This is a capital expense.

Bank reconciliation statements

6   Sally calculates her bank balance to be £160 positive, however her bank statement shows a different amount. Having considered the following items, calculate the balance on Sally's bank statement.

(i)   A cheque that Sally paid into the bank for £40 is still outstanding.
(ii)   A cheque for £60 paid by Sally to Molly has not yet been presented.
(iii) Sally has forgotten to record a cash withdrawal of £30.
(iv) When Sally inspects her bank statement she sees that the bank has deducted charges of £15 from her account.

A   £95
B   £135
C   £185
D   £225

Answer

B   Sally's correct cash book figure is £115 being £160 less the bank charges and withdrawal which she had not accounted for. Therefore the correct bank statement figure is £115 plus the cheque to Molly which has not been presented, less the lodgement which has not yet been processed.

i.e. 115 + 60 − 40 = 135

Double entry transactions

7   Norman works in a manufacturing company and is preparing his first set of accounts. He is confused about the distinction between various items in the balance sheet.

Advise Norman as to which of the following he should classify as current assets.

(i)   stock
(ii)   creditors
(iii) debtors
(iv) motor vehicles.

A   All four
B   (i), (ii) and (iii)
C   (ii), (iii) and (iv)
D   (i) and (iii).

Answer

D   Creditors are a current liability and motor vehicles are fixed assets.

Double entry transactions

8 Pimlico & Co owe Vauxhall Ltd for some goods it recently bought. Pimlico & Co are settling the invoice early and are getting a discount.

What is the correct double entry for this in Vauxhall Ltd's books?

A   Debit Vauxhall Ltd, Credit Bank, Credit Discount received.
B   Debit Vauxhall Ltd, Debit Discount received, Credit Bank.
C   Debit Bank, Credit Discount allowed, Credit Pimlico & Co.
D   Debit Bank, Debit Discount allowed, Credit Pimlico & Co.

Answer

D   Vauxhall is receiving the money therefore it must be a debit to the bank. The discount allowed is also a debit. The credit is to clear the debtors ledger for Pimlico's account.

Double entry

9 The opening balance at 1 June on Northolt Ltd's debtors ledger showed total amounts owed as £6,478. During June Northolt made sales of £53,998, half of these sales were for cash. At the end of June Northolt's customers owed £10,492.

How much cash did Northolt receive from its customers during June?

A   £58,012
B   £49,984
C   £31,013
D   £22,985

Answer

D

Debtors ledger			
Debtors b/f	64,785		
credit sales	26,999		
		therefore cash received	**22,985**
		Debtors c/f	10,492

Accounts analysis including age analysis

10 Waterloo Ltd uses the following proforma for its aged creditors report.

Supplier	Total owed	< 30 days	30–60 days	60–90 days	> 90 days

In the creditors ledger cash paid and credit notes received are matched against invoices.

From the two creditors ledgers given below which is the correct classification of amounts owing as at 31 December.

Jack Limited

12 Dec c/note	612·94	6 Oct invoice	293·10
14 Dec cash	212·15	12 Oct invoice	612·94
		15 Oct invoice	409·17
		17 Nov invoice	212·15
		29 Nov invoice	65·67
		10 Dec invoice	97·56

Vera & Co.

24 Nov cash	67·12	14 Sep invoice	67·12
14 Dec c/note	41·91	30 Sep invoice	42·39
14 Dec cash	123·45	10 Oct invoice	412·00
21 Dec cash	312·41	17 Oct invoice	312·41
		25 Oct invoice	41·91
		5 Nov invoice	296·15
		18 Nov invoice	101·13
		1 Dec invoice	123·45
		13 Dec invoice	444·32

	< 30 days	30–60 days	60–90 days	> 90 days
A	£ –	£541·88	£462·95	£1,114·27
B	£ –	£541·88	£462·95	£1,156·18
C	£541·88	£462·95	£1,114·27	£42·39
D	£541·88	£462·95	£1,156·18	£109·51

Answer

C Outstanding December invoices are classed as <30 days hence A and B are incorrect. The only invoices classed as >90 days are September invoices hence £42·39 is in this category and D is incorrect.

ACCA Accounting Technician Examination

Level A

Paper 2

Office Practice and Procedures

MCQ Paper:	
Time allowed	2 hours
Sample Questions Only	

The Association of Chartered Certified Accountants

NOTE: These are Sample Questions

Office equipment....communication of text

1   Tarquin, a colleague in the marketing department, has been asked to design a company letterhead. He is unsure what information should be contained in the letterhead and has asked for your help.

From the following list of Tarquin's ideas, which is least likely to be included in the letterhead?

A   Telephone, fax numbers and e-mail address.
B   The company's mission statement.
C   The company's name and address.
D   An indication of the nature of the organisation e.g. partnership, public limited company.

Answer

B   A,C and D are vital pieces of information for inclusion on a letterhead.

Office equipment....communication of text

2   You have been asked to write three letters on behalf of your boss.
Letter 1: – To a government department.
Letter 2: – To a customer named Mrs Valerie Jones who has written a letter of complaint.
Letter 3: – To Alan, one of your boss' ex-colleagues to arrange a meeting and a round of golf.

How should you start and finish each letter?

	Letter 1	Letter 2	Letter 3
A	Dear Department Yours faithfully	Dear Valerie Yours sincerely	Dear Sir Yours faithfully
B	Dear Sir/Madam Yours sincerely	Dear Mrs Jones Yours sincerely	Dear Alan Yours sincerely
C	Dear Sir/Madam Yours faithfully	Dear Madam Yours sincerely	Dear Alan Kind regards
D	Dear Sir/Madam Yours faithfully	Dear Mrs Jones Yours sincerely	Dear Alan Kind regards

Answer

D   A is incorrect – you should never address 'the department'.
B and C are incorrect – Dear Sir/Madam should be accompanied with yours faithfully.

Maintaining information storage systems

3   Jack is reorganising the filing system for the accounts function.

Which of the following documents is Jack least likely to file in the sales ledger department?

A   Copy sales invoices
B   copy credit notes issued
C   supplier statements
D   details of cheques received.

Answer

C   Supplier statements would be filed in the purchase ledger department.

The types and use of different information sources

4   You have been asked to write a report outlining the qualities of good information.

Which of the following would you not include in the report?

A   The information should be complete.
B   The information should be communicated via an appropriate channel.
C   The information should be understandable.
D   The information should be communicated to everyone in the organisation.

Answer

D   Information should be communicated to the right person/people to ensure that people do not waste time reading information that has no relevance to them.

Health and safety

5   The Health and Safety Office employs inspectors to ensure that its regulations are implemented in businesses. You are applying for a job at this office and have just received a description of the job from a recruitment consultant. From your background reading on the Health and Safety Office you are sure that one of the powers of inspectors that they have described is incorrect.

Which one do you think the recruitment consultant has included in error?

Inspectors have the power to:

A   Fire the Health and Safety officer if it is clear that he/she has neglected their role.
B   Enter premises at reasonable times, or at any time if a dangerous situation may exist.
C   Take measurements and photographs as considered necessary.
D   To take samples of substances and of the atmosphere.

Answer

A   This is not a power of an inspector.

Methods of and efficient use of routine business communication...

6   The process of communication can be modelled in to a flow chart.

Which of the following correctly charts the process of communication?

A   The message => decoding the message => transmitting the message => receiving the message => encoding the message =>action => feedback.

B   The message => encoding the message => receiving the message => transmitting the message =>decoding the message => feedback => action.

C   The message => transmitting the message => encoding the message => receiving the message => decoding the message => action => feedback.

D   The message => encoding the message => transmitting the message => receiving the message => decoding the message => action => feedback.

Answer

D

Effective visitor relationships

7 You usually work in the sales ledger department but due to an unexpected staff shortage you have been asked to cover the reception area over the lunchtime period. A visitor enters the building and announces that he wants to meet the finance director to discuss some accounting packages which he knows would revolutionise the production of accounts in your company. You ascertain that the visitor does not have an appointment.

Which of the following responses would you consider to be most appropriate?

A   Tell the visitor that the company has no need of new software.
B   Telephone the finance director to advise him that he has a visitor in reception.
C   Advise the visitor to leave his business card and details of the accounting packages, and that he should telephone the finance director in a few days.   You then pass these details on to the finance director.
D   Advise the visitor to wait while you go and find the finance director.

Answer

C   A – you do not know that this is correct.
B – The FD is unlikely to be happy at being interrupted with this query particularly as this visitor has arrived without an appointment.
D – worse than B because you would leave the reception area understaffed or unattended.

Maintaining information storage systems

8 **Which of the following do you consider to be the least important feature of a storage or filing system?**

A   It must be easy to determine precisely where a document should be filed.
B   If a document is required it must be easy to determine where that document is currently filed.
C   Retrieval of information must be relatively easy in physical terms.
D   All information must be archived once it has been on file for three years.

Answer

D   Some information may be referred to often despite being written say three years ago. A policy for archiving is recommended but care is needed to ensure that useful documents are not archived.

Maintaining information storage systems

9 **Which of the following pieces of information is least likely to be held on an active file in a sales department?**

A   Customer address, credit limit and bank details.
B   Documents relating to current contracts.
C   Current amounts outstanding
D   Details of current years sales.

Answer

A   These details are unlikely to change.

Methods of and efficient use of routine business communication

10 John is designing an in-house training course to teach staff to make effective notes. He wants to give staff three key points to remember.

Which point should not be on John's list?

A   The notes should be as concise as possible but must contain all the key points.
B   The notes should always include the note taker's opinions on the original material.
C   The notes should be legible
D   The notes should be comprehensible.

Answer

B   Notes should reach the same conclusions as the original material with no input, in terms of opinions, from the person making the notes.

End of Question Paper

ACCA Accounting Technician Examination

Level B

Paper 1

Maintaining Financial Records and Accounts

Essay Question Paper	
Time allowed	2 hours
ALL THREE questions are compulsory and MUST be attempted	

The Association of Chartered Certified Accountants

ALL THREE questions are compulsory and MUST be answered

1   Appendix 1 contains the trial balance extracted from the books of Alexander Amos at 31 March 1997 (the year end). Appendix 1 is reproduced in your answer book and should be used in answering question 1 parts 1d) and 2. All workings should be shown. You should round figures to the nearest £.

The following background information about his manual bookkeeping system is relevant: the general ledger contains the sales and purchase ledger control accounts and with the cash book is a complete double entry system. The individual sales and purchase ledgers are memorandum.

Part I

Required:

(a) Describe when and why a trial balance might be extracted.   (2 marks)

(b) List and explain the main types of error which a balanced trial balance may conceal.   (4 marks)

(c) Describe five tasks commonly carried out to monitor the accurate operation of the accounting system.

(5 marks)

The trial balance in Appendix 1 shows a suspense account balance of £645. An investigation has revealed the following:

(i)   Receipts from credit customers in September 1996 totalling £3,182 have been posted as £3,812 in the sales ledger control account.

(ii)   A cheque received for £425 from credit customer B. Burton in February 1997 was returned unpaid by the bank in March 1997. The cash book balance was adjusted when the March bank reconciliation was done - no other entries were made.

(iii) An amount of £1,583 for re-decoration has been incorrectly posted to fixtures and fittings account instead of repairs account.

(iv) An addition error in the analysis columns of the purchases day book in January 1997 resulted in total purchases for the month being recorded as £2,516 instead of £2,606. This was the only posting affected by the error.

(v)   Stock purchase invoice XX11 from Zigzag Ltd for £588 was fully recorded in February 1997 in the purchase day book. An amended invoice was later issued by Zigzag for £705 which was also recorded in the purchase day book. No credit note had been received.

(vi) A cheque received for £500 on 30 September 1996 for the sale of car registration number F602 SWS had been posted to suspense account because the cashier was unsure how to deal with it.

Required:

(d) Write up the journal entries to correct the above errors; and

(e) Enter the adjustments appropriately on the extended trial balance in your answer book.

(24 marks)

(35 marks)

Part II

The following information has been collected for the preparation of the year-end accounts of Alexander Amos:
- A review of the sales ledger showed that a number of balances were overdue:

		Overdue
Alpha Ltd	£86	8 months
J. Brown	£245	5 months
Dan's Health Store	£105	4 months
F. Miller	£46	6 months
Page Ltd	£423	3 months

It was decided that those six months overdue and over should be written off. A provision for doubtful debts of 2% of the remaining balances is to be made.

The stock sheets at 31 March 1997 showed a total inventory of £23,592.
- Subsequent double checking had revealed the following:

  - Page 15 was over cast by £1,000.
  - Slow-moving stock items costing £3,100 were shown at cost but had been included in the April sales at 90% of cost price.

- Depreciation is provided as follows:

Fixtures and fittings	10%	straight line
Motor vehicles	20%	reducing balance

  It is the policy to charge a full years' depreciation in the year of purchase and none in the year of sale.

Fixtures and fittings were all acquired on 1 April 1991, when the business was started, at a cost of £25,000.

There are three motor vehicles which were acquired as follows:

    M904 ABC acquired 1 April 1994 for £12,000;
    N962 XYZ acquired 1 September 1995 for £15,000;
    F602 SWS acquired 1 July 1993 for £10,000 (disposed of on 30
    September 1996 - see part 1)

An examination of the purchase and expense invoices revealed:

- Annual car insurance had been renewed on 1 October 1996 at a cost of £1,500.
- Purchase invoices to the value of £2,456 for goods in stock at 31 March 1997 had not been processed at that date.

Required:

(a) **Enter the adjustments appropriately on the extended trial balance in your answer book.**

(15 marks)

(b) **Extend the figures in the extended trial balance in your answer book into the profit and loss account and balance sheet columns and balance.**

(15 marks)

(30 marks)

(65 marks)

2 **(a)** Explain what is meant by the matching concept (2 marks)

(b) Identify three other generally accepted accounting concepts and give a brief explanation of each.

(6 marks)

(c) PDS operates a manual bookkeeping system. An examination of the accounts paid for motor expenses reveals the following:

Petrol	(paid one month in arrears) to June 97	£1,225
	June 1997 account received and paid July 97	£165
Car insurance	(started 1 October 1996) for year to 30 September 97	£1,200
Car licenses	(paid September 1996) for six months to 31 March 1997	£80
	(paid March 1997) for year to 31 March 1998	£140

Servicing and repairs accounts amounted to £1,500 for work carried out and invoiced in the period to 30 June 1997. An invoice for £350 was received in August 1997 for work carried out in June 1997.

Required:

(i) to make the appropriate entries in the motor expenses account for the year ended 30 June 1997;

(ii) to balance off the account as at that date using an accruals account and a prepayments account; and

(iii) to make the opening entries in the motor expenses account as at 1 July 1997.

(12 marks)

(20 marks)

3 You have been asked to go and help a client, Peter Robin, who set up in business on 1 April 1997, and who is unsure whether he is recording his transactions correctly. His sales are normally for cash but he occasionally allows credit to regular customers – these sales are registered through the till when the customer pays. He pays many of his expenses in cash and then banks the remainder, leaving a float of £200.

Peter has only been keeping cash book records as he does not understand the double entry process.
His cash book for the three months to 30 June 1997, in summary, shows the following:

Receipts	Received from sales £	Banking £	Payments	Cash £	Bank £
Per till rolls	34,164		Suppliers	12,950	6,500
Per pay-in slips		12,450	Drawings	6,000	2,000
			Wages	2,850	
			Sundry expenses	100	935

Peter is able to give you the following additional information:
A cheque received in refund from a supplier for £450 was included in bankings but not put through the till
Cash in hand at 30 June 1997 was £200
Customers who had received goods on credit, owed him £320 at 30 June 1997.

Required:

(a) Balance the cash account at 30 June 1997 (giving workings and explanations); (14 marks)

(b) Calculate the sales for the three months to 30 June 1997. (5 marks)

(15 marks)

End of Question Paper

Answers

1   Part I

(a) On both manual and computerised systems, a trial balance may be extracted at the end of each accounting period as a first step in preparing the period/year profit and loss account and balance sheet. Additionally, on a manual system, it will be used to check that double entry bookkeeping has been carried out i.e. that the trial balance is balanced.

(b) A balanced trial balance may conceal errors of:

- omission – transactions have been omitted from the ledger accounts;
- commission/principle – transactions have been entered in the books but posted, wholly or partly, to the wrong accounts;
- entry – the amount posted is incorrect but to the correct accounts;
- compensating – one or more errors cancel each other out.

(c) Tasks commonly used to monitor the accurate operation of the accounting system include:-

bank reconciliations;
petty cash count/reconciliation;
reconciliation of purchase ledger accounts to suppliers statements;
reconciliations of purchase/sales ledgers to control accounts;
regular clearance of balances in suspense account;
clearance of wages and other control accounts;
sales tax reconciliation;
reconciliation of plant to plant register and to fixed asset accounts;
internal audit.

(d) Journal

		Dr	Cr
(i)	Sales ledger control	630	
	Suspense		630
	Receipts from credit customers incorrectly posted to sales ledger control		
(ii)	Sales ledger control	425	
	Suspense		425
	Cheque from B. Burton returned unpaid		
(iii)	Repairs	1,583	
	Fixtures and fittings		1,583
	March expenditure on repairs incorrectly posted to fixtures and fittings		
(iv)	Purchases	90	
	Suspense		90
	Correction of an error in the purchases daybook January 1997		
(v)	Purchase ledger control	588	
	Purchases		588
	Reversal of invoice 2004 from Zigzag Ltd recorded February 1997		
(vi)	Suspense	500	
	Motor vehicle disposal account		500
	Proceeds of sale of car registration F602 SWS on 30 September 1996		

(e) See completed extended trial balance.

Part II

See completed extended trial balance overleaf

Workings

(a) Debts to be written off:

	Alpha Ltd	86
	F. Miller	46
		132

Provision for bad debts:

	Sales ledger control account	£9,680
	Adjustments from Part I (i) and (ii)	1,055
	Adjustment above	(132)
		10,603
	Provision required 2%	212

i.e. reduction of   810 (1,022 – 212)

(b)

Original stock sheets	23,592
Adjustment for page 15 overcast	(1,000)
Adjustment to net realisable value for sale items	(310)
Closing stock value	22,282

(c) *Fixtures and fittings:*   depreciation 10% £25,000   2,500

Motor vehicles:

	Cost	Depreciation	NBV
F602 SWS Disposal			
y/e 31 March 1994	10,000	2,000	8,000
y/e 31 March 1995		1,600	6,400
y/e 31 March 1996		1,280	5,120
Book values at date of sale	10,000	4,880	5,120
Remaining vehicles	27,000	7,320	19,680
Per trial balance	37,000	12,200	24,800
Depreciation for y/e 31 March 1997	(19,680 x 20%)		3,936

(d) Annual car insurance: six months prepaid (6/12 x 1,500)   750

Purchase invoices not processed   accrual   2,456

21

Appendix I

Alexander Amos – Trial balance as at 31 March 1997

	Balances per ledger		Adjustments Q1 Part I		Adjustments Q1 Part II				Profit and Loss a/c		Balance sheet	
	Dr	Cr	Dr	Cr	Dr	Cr	Accrued	Prepaid	Dr	Cr	Dr	Cr
Fixtures and fittings	26,583			1,583							25,000	
Depreciation on fixtures and fittings at 1 April 1996		12,500				2,500						15,000
Motor vehicles	37,000					10,000					27,000	
Depreciation on motor vehicles at 1 April 1996		12,200			4,880	3,936						11,256
Stock at 1 April 1996	20,345								20,345			
Sales ledger control account	9,680		630 425			132					10,603	
Bank balance	2,125										2,125	
Cash balance	720										720	
Purchase ledger control account		7,900	588									7,312
Capital account		30,000										30,000
Sales		126,458								126,458		
Purchases	53,772		90	588			2,456		55,730			
Repairs	684		1,583						2,267			
Provision for doubtful debts at 1 April 1996		1,022			810							212
Bad debts written off	408				132	810				270		
Motor expenses	5,378							750	4,628			
Light and heat	1,980								1,980			
Printing and stationery	760								760			
Wages	18,328								18,328			
Drawings	11,672										11,672	
Suspense account	645		500	630 425 90								
Closing stock					22,282	22,282				22,282	22,282	
Depreciation for year F & F					2,500				2,500			
Depreciation for year MV					3,936				3,936			
Disposal motor vehicle				500	10,000	4,880			4,620			
Accrued/prepaid							2,456	750			750	2,456
Totals	190,080	190,080	3,816	3,816	44,540	44,540	2,456	750	115,094	149,010	100,152	66,236
Profit for year									33,916			33,916
									149,010	149,010	100,152	100,152

2 (a) The matching concept refers to the matching of expenditure to income realised in the period for which the accounts are being prepared or to the accounting period itself.

(b) Other generally accepted accounting concepts include:

- Prudence – the principle that profits should not be anticipated before they are realised and that losses should be provided for wherever they are probable.

- Consistency – the principle that the same accounting policies and practises should be adopted from year to year unless circumstances have changed.

- Going concern – the principle that accounts should be prepared with the underlying assumption that the business will continue to exist into the future.

- Substance over form – accounts should reflect the substance of transactions rather than the legal form of those transactions if this gives a more true and fair view.

(c)

Motor expenses account

		£			£
1 Jul	Cash - creditors	1,225	30 Jun	Prepaid insurance	300
to 30	Cash - insurance	1,200	30 Jun	Prepaid licenses	105
Jun	Cash - licenses	220			
	Cash - service, repairs	1,500	30 Jun	Profit and Loss A/c	4,090
30 Jun	Accrued petrol	165			
30 Jun	Accrued service, repairs	350			
		4,495			4,495
1 Jul	Prepayments a/c	405	1 Jul	Accruals a/c	575

Prepayments

		£			£
30 Jun	Motor expenses	300			
30 Jun	Motor expenses	105	30 Jun	Balance c/d	405
		405			405
1 Jul	Balance b/d	405	1 Jul	Motor expenses	405

Accruals

		£			£
			30 Jun	Motor expenses	165
30 Jun	Balance c/d	465	30 Jun	Motor expenses	350
		465			465
1 Jul	Motor expenses	465	1 Jul	Balance b/d	465

3 **(a)**

Cash account

		£			£
1 Apl	Sales (till rolls)	34,164	1 Apl	Bankings	12,450
to	Cheque refund	450	to	Cash purchases	12,950
30 Jun			30 Jun	Drawings	6,000
				Wages	2,850
				Sundry expenses	100
			30 Jun	Balance c/d	200
					34,550
			30 Jun	Unaccounted balance (see below)	64
		34,614			34,614

The cash unaccounted for (£64) will require further investigation. It may be cash payments unrecorded, drawings unrecorded, or sales refunds (cash) unrecorded. In practise, if the balance remains unexplained (i.e. no vouchers can be found) it would normally be treated as drawings.

(b) Sales for the quarter:

	£
Per till rolls	34,164
Credit sales not yet paid	320
	34,484

End of Question Paper

Marks

1	**Part I**	**(a)**	working paper	1	
			balance check	1	
				—	2
		(b)	4 types of error		4
		(c)	5 tasks		5
		(d)	6 journals	12	
			6 narratives	6	
			12 entries TB	6	
				—	24
					35

	Part II	Calculation debt w/o	0.5	
		Entries TB	1	
		Sales Ledger for provision	1	
		Provision	1	
		Change in provision	1	
		Entries TB	1	
		Adjusted closing stock	1	
		Entries TB	1	
		Deprecation F&F	1	
		Deprecation MV Disposal	1.5	
		Disposal entries TB	1	
		Deprecation MV	1	
		Depreciation entries TB	1.5	
		Insurance prepayment	0.5	
		Accrual+prepayments TB	1	
			—	15
		Completion of P&L and profit computation	7.5	
		Completion of balance sheet	7.5	
			—	15
				65

2	**(a)**		link to income	1	
			link to period	1	
				—	2
	(b)		3 concepts	3	
			3 explanations	3	
				—	6
	(c)	(i)	entries in account	2	
		(ii)	motor expenses accruals	2	
			motor expenses prepayments	2	
			motor expenses trfr P&L	1	
			motor expenses a/c balance	1	
			accrual a/c balance +c/d	1	
			prepayment a/c balance +c/d	1	
		(iii)	transfer balances to motor expense a/c	2	
				—	12
					20

3 **(a)** Entries in cash account   8
            Balancing cash account
            + identification of missing   2
            explanations   4
                                            —
                                            14

     (b) 3 month sales   1
                                            —
                                            15

ACCA Accounting Technician Examination

Level B

Paper 2

Cost Accounting Systems

Essay Question Paper	
Time allowed	2 hours
ALL FOUR questions are compulsory and MUST be attempted	

The Association of Chartered Certified Accountants

ALL FOUR questions are compulsory and MUST be answered

1   A small manufacturing business comprises three production departments undertaking machining, assembly and finishing operations and support departments for stores and for buildings. A production period budgeted cost and resource profile for each of the five departments is as follows:

	Machining	Assembly	Finishing	Stores	Buildings
Direct costs £ 350,000	250,000	185,000	125,000	320,000	
Space (metres)	500		400	450	650
Material (volume)	12,000	35,000	5,000		
Direct labour hours			6,000	7,500	
Direct machine hours	8,000				

The business is to introduce a total absorption costing system in which costs are absorbed to production jobs using budgeted direct machine hours for the machining department and budgeted direct labour hours for the assembly and finishing departments.

Required:

(a) **Calculate absorption rates for each of the three production departments which will collectively result in the total cost of the business being absorbed to production jobs.**

(18 marks)

(b) **Briefly explain the reasons for your choice of method for apportioning the stores and buildings support departments to the three production departments.**

(6 marks)

(c) During the actual production period the finishing department worked 7,000 direct labour hours as against the plan of 7,500 direct labour hours.

Describe how the accounting system might deal with any resulting under-recovery of costs.

(6 marks)

(30 marks)

2   You have been asked by the transport manager of your organisation to provide a suitable graph to be used to illustrate the change in costs when operating a goods distribution vehicle at various annual mileage rates. The costs per vehicle are as follows:

–   insurance at £2,000 per annum

–   depreciation charges at an annual rate of £3,000 plus 10 pence per mile for each mile travelled in excess of 14,000 miles per annum

–   maintenance costs of 15 pence per mile

–   fuel costs 45 pence per litre and vehicles consume at the rate of five miles per litre

–   a road users licence at £1,500 per annum.

Required:

(a) **Draw a graph which can be used to identify the *total operating cost* of the goods distribution vehicle against miles travelled. Your graph should cover a range between 10,000 to 20,000 miles per annum.**

(20 marks)

(b) **Use your graph to help calculate the *operating cost per mile* at 13,000 miles per annum and 17,000 miles per annum (show all of your workings).**

(5 marks)

(25 marks)

Note: marks will be awarded for neatness and clarity of presentation.

3 Listed below is a record of a series of stock transactions undertaken by a wholesale business during the month of March for one of its stock items.

Stock Item ABC	Units	Value £
1 March opening stock	350	2,800·00
3 March receipt	500	4,125·00
8 March issue	650	
10 March receipt	500	4,325·00
18 March issue	425	
23 March issue	100	
25 March receipt	500	3,950·00

Required:

(a) Calculate the value of each of the three issues of Stock Item ABC using the last in, first out (LIFO) method and the first in, first out (FIFO) method.

(12 marks)

(b) Assuming there were no further transaction for stock item ABC calculate the closing stock values which would result from the LIFO and from the FIFO methods.

(4 marks)

(c) An alternative to the LIFO and FIFO methods would be to carry all stock items at a value based on a standard price. Assuming such a system and that the opening stock is carried at a standard price of £8·00 per item:

(i) explain how the materials accounting system would deal with a difference between the actual price of a receipt and the standard price

(7 marks)

(ii) calculate the value of the closing stock of item ABC at the standard price of £8·00 per unit.

(2 marks)

(25 marks)

4 Listed below are six commonly used terms in cost accounting systems.

Required:

Select and briefly describe the meaning of FOUR of the terms. Each selection will carry equal marks.

(a) Stepped fixed cost

(b) Joint and by-products

(c) Labour utilisation rate or ratio

(d) Stockholding margin of safety

(e) Standard product cost

(f) Period cost.

(20 marks)

End of Question Paper

Answers

1 **(a)** Calculation of absorption rates by cost apportionment:

	Machining	*Assembly*	*Finishing*	*Stores*	*Buildings*
Direct costs	350,000	250,000	185,000	125,000	320,000
Buildings apportioned by area	80,000	64,000	72,000	104,000	(320,000)
				229,000	
Stores apportioned by material value	52,846	154,135	22,019	(229,000)	
Total cost	482,846	468,135	279,019		
Absorbed by:					
Machine/labour hours	8,000	6,000	7,500		
Absorption rate per hour	£60·36	£78·02	£37·20		

(b) Service department costs must be apportioned to production departments to enable a cost recovery rate to be calculated which absorbs total cost to production units. The method chosen should balance materiality against complexity of calculation and use the most relevant 'cost driver' or cost linkage between the support or overhead cost and the production department.

Bearing in mind such criteria the step down method was chosen as the best balance between simplicity of calculation (as opposed to the repeated distribution method) while reflecting reciprocal services between support departments (as opposed to ignoring reciprocal relationships and apportioning direct).

The most appropriate apportionment rates were space occupied for buildings services and materials value for the stores department. Note that alternatives for stores could have been stores transactions or the volume of materials but such information was not made available in the question.

(c) If we assume that the direct costs of the finishing department and apportioned costs are all fixed then the under-absorption of costs for the period would be 500 hours at £37·20 per hour or £18,600.

There are two possible methods of dealing with the under-absorption. The amount could be transferred to the profit and loss account for the period thus resulting in a profit reduction for the period or alternatively transferred to a cost under/over absorption account which would be used to accumulate variations during each period of the financial year with the balance being transferred to the year end profit and loss account. The latter method avoids period to period fluctuations which may cancel out by the end of the year.

2 **(a)** An approach is to calculate the total cost at three points (there being a change in cost pattern due to depreciation at 14,000 miles) and use these three points to draw the graph as follows:

	10,000	14,000	20,000
Insurance at £2,000 per annum	2,000	2,000	2,000
Depreciation (annual at £3,000)	3,000	3,000	3,000
Depreciation (10p per mile over 14,000 pa)	0	0	600
Maintenance (15p per mile)	1,500	2,100	3,000
Fuel (5 mpl at 45 ppl)	900	1,260	1,800
Road use license £1,500 per annum	1,500	1,500	1,500
Total cost	8,900	9,860	11,900

Please see graph on opposite page.

(b) Using the lines marked for illustration on the attached graph the total cost at 13,000 miles per annum is £9,620 giving a cost of £0·74 per mile (£9,620 / 13,000) and at 17,000 miles £10,880 giving a cost of £0·64 per mile (£10,880 / 17,000).

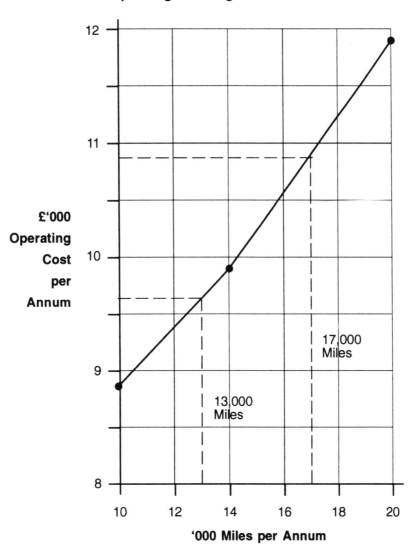

Total Operating Costs against Miles Travelled

£'000 Operating Cost per Annum (y-axis: 8 to 12)

'000 Miles per Annum (x-axis: 10 to 20)

13,000 Miles

17,000 Miles

3 **(a)** Material issue values under LIFO and FIFO are as follows:

		Units O/S plus receipts	Issues	Value £	Bal'ce Units	LIFO£	FIFO£
P0	opening stock	350		2,800·00	350		
P1	receipt	500		4,125·00	850		
P2	issue		650		200	5,325·00	5,275·00
P3	receipt	500		4,325·00	700		
P4	issue		425		275	3,676·25	3,596·25
P5	issue		100		175	848·75	865·00
P6	receipt	500		3,950·00	675		
P7	closing stock				675	5,350·00	5,463·75

Note that the answer assumes a rolling valuation on LIFO, that is, the issue on the 23rd (P5) does not anticipate the 25th receipt (P6).

(b) From the table provided in part (a) it can be seen that the closing values are as follows:

LIFO   500 x £7·90 + 175 x £8·00 = £5,350·00

FIFO   500 x £7·90 + 175 x £8·65 = £5,463·75

(c) (i) Using a standard price for materials receipts and issues would require that the difference, if any, between standard and actual be identified at the point of receipt and the resulting variance transferred to a materials variance account.

For example, the receipt of 500 units on the third at a value of £4,125·00 (suggesting £8·25 per unit) would give rise to an adverse materials acquisition variance of £125 (£4,125 as against £4,000 or 500 at £8) which would result in a debit to stock of £4,000 and a debit to the materials variance account of £125. Note that if the materials variances were significant and expected to be permanent then the business may consider adjusting the standard materials price to reflect the new circumstances.

The balance on the materials variance account would be taken to profit and loss account either at the end of the production period or at the year end.

(ii) Under a standard costing systems the closing stock would be 675 units at the standard price of £8·00 per unit being £5,400·00.

4 (a) Stepped fixed costs are fixed costs which do not change with changes in the level of output but rather with an identified break point at which an additional unit of resource is acquired. For example, a business may lease four identical machines for producing components. The lease charges will thus be a fixed cost for each production period. If production rises to the point where the four machines are working at maximum output then any production beyond this point will require the acquisition of a fifth machine. It follows that costs will rise (step) up to the fixed cost of five leased machines.

(b) Joint and by-products. A feature of process costing is that more than one product may be produced from the manufacturing process. For example, in an oil refinery the refining process may result in a range of products including tar, kerosene, petrol etc. Joint and by-products are generally defined in relation to their relative market value and may differ between industries. Joint products are those which have a relatively high market value and are recognisable as saleable products while by-products are those which arise incidentally from the process and have a marginal sale or market value such as the production of sawdust in a sawmill.

(c) Labour utilisation rate or ratio. Is a measure which can be used to monitor the efficient use of labour, that is, actual working time being utilised in producing output as opposed to what may be called lost or idle time. Lost time can occur through a variety of reasons depending on the type of business. For example, in a construction business idle time can arise due to bad weather while in a production operation idle time could be due to machine breakdown, waiting for materials or poor production scheduling. In calculating a standard labour utilisation rate allowance will be made for normal lost time. In other words the target is one which is achievable rather than theortical.

(d) Stockholding margin of safety. It may be assumed that one of the objectives of a stores department is to minimise stockholding costs while at the same time avoiding disruption or loss of sales arising from stockouts. In deciding the ordering pattern for stocks (order size, frequency, minimum stock level) the risk of delay in delivery or supply must be estimated. The greater the risk then the higher must be the margin of safety. For example, if the order to delivery schedule is five days but could in certain circumstances be as long as eight days then a margin of safety of three days times the average daily usage would ensure a margin which should avoid stockouts.

(e) Standard product cost. Many businesses use standard product costing as a system of cost planning and control. The standard cost is built up for control purposes based on an attainable level (rather than ideal) of performance assuming achievable levels of efficiency (in using labour, materials and overheads). It follows that the standard cost is the average cost given the achievement of efficient production operations. The comparison of standard cost to actual cost provides an accounting variance which can be used for the purpose of management reporting.

(f) Period costs are those costs which are identified with non-production activity rather than production activity. Examples being sales and administration expenses. As such period costs are not included in the valuation of stock and work in progress (unexpired product costs) but are treated as an expense and carried to the profit and loss account in the period in which they are incurred. This can be contrasted with product costs in which only the expired (or sold) product costs are expensed in the period, the unexpired portion being carried as an asset into the next production period.

End of Question Paper

Technician Examination – Paper B2
Cost Accounting Systems

Marking Scheme

Marks

1 (a) Apportionment buildings – 1 mark per department, method 2   to 5
Apportionment stores – 1 mark per department, method 2   to 5
Correct total   2
Absorption rate – 3 x 2 marks   6
    18

(b) Identification of cost drivers   1 to 2
Treatment of reciprocal services   2 to 3
Choice of method for buildings and stores   3 to 4
    6

(c) Illustration of under-absorption   1 to 2
Description of method   3 to 4
Identification of two possible treatments   1 to 2
    6

    30

2 (a) General layout of graph (neatness)   to 2
Suitable scaling and labeling   3 to 4
Cost calculation at each of three location points   9 to 12
Correct plotting   6 to 8
    20

(b) For each example
Location of correct total   1 to 2
Calculation of cost per mile   1 to 2
    5

    25

3 (a) For each of three transaction by two methods:
Calculation LIFO   2
Calculation FIFO   2
    12

(b) Calculation of closing stock value:
LIFO   2
FIFO   2
    4

(c) (i) Identification of Materials Variance Account   1
Illustration of variance   2 to 3
Description of transfer to a/c and thence to P&L   4 to 5

(ii) Calculation of correct closing stock   2
    9

    25

4 For each of four from six terms:
Very generalised indication of use of the term only   to 1
Brief but correct, single sentence description   to 2
Expanded description using a suitable illustration   to 4
    20

ACCA Accounting Technician Examination

Level B

Paper 3

Information Technology Processes

Essay Question Paper	
Time allowed	2 hours
ALL FOUR questions are compulsory and MUST be attempted	

The Association of Chartered Certified Accountants

ALL FOUR questions are compulsory and MUST be answered

1   You have been made responsible for the operational management of the small computer system in your accounting office. The system operates a standard accounts package comprising sales, purchase and general ledger modules and supports four users. The general manager of your organisation has informed you that she is worried about the security of the system,

   Required:

   (a) Briefly describe the types of security risk which should be protected against.   (10 marks)

   (b) Produce a checklist for the general manager which identifies the potential risks and the controls which help protect against them occurring.   (15 marks)

                                                                                             (25 marks)

2   You have recently taken control of the accounts office of a small business and plan to purchase a personal computer (PC) for general accounts, spreadsheets and access to on-line services. You have placed an order for the machine but the order has been sent back by the owner of the business. He has suggested that a much cheaper machine would suffice and has asked you to explain the significance of aspects of the specification of the machine you have ordered.

   Required:

   Write a short note to the owner explaining the meaning and significance of the following aspects of the PC you have ordered:

   (a) Windows operating environment

   (b) in-built modem

   (c) CD-ROM drive

   (d) 200 MHz processor

   (e) 3 Gbyte hard disk   **(25 marks)**

3   You are a section leader in an accounts office and have been informed that a team of systems analysts will be visiting your department as part of a systems feasibility study to upgrade the existing computer-based systems.

   Required:

   (a) Describe the methods/techniques which you would expect the systems analysts to use in investigating the work of your department   (15 marks)

   (b) What role do you feel that you should play in this investigation phase.   (10 marks)

                                                                                             (25 marks)

4   You have been asked to assist in the specification for the office automation components (hardware and software) to meet the requirements of an accounts and administration office. There are 10 members of staff in the accounts office and they support the work of a medium-sized manufacturing company with 200 employees.

   Required:

   List and describe the hardware and software components which would most probably form a part of the specification Where possible you should give names of suitable proprietary products.

                                                                                             (25 marks)

End of Question Paper

Answers

1 (a) The main security risks to guard against are accidental or deliberate threats to:
  (i)   confidentiality by the disclosure of information which may lead to prosecution under any Data Protection legislation, embarrassing publicity or loss of commercial competitive advantage
  (ii) modification of data which could lead to fraud or mistakes which cause loss of business or expensive rectification
  (iii) interruption of service because of hardware or software being unavailable because of physical problems (fire, flood, power failure) or software problems (virus, file corruption etc).

(b) *Such a checklist would cover:*
  Threat: Disclosure: remedy - need to control access to computer systems and data by:
  – siting of computer (public unable to see screen, possible physical safeguards to control access to computer (e.g. locks etc.))
  – use of passwords to limit access and functions available to authorised persons
  – continual controls over useage of passwords; frequency of change etc.
  – controls over stationery such as payslips and cheques
  – control over confidential printed output (numbered copies, controlled circulation lists, shredding of copies after use)
  – control over magnetic media holding sensitive information (e.g. floppy disks and cassette back up copies of files)
  – staffing and disciplinary measures – e.g. policies on recruitment, supervision and disciplinary action taken over unauthorised disclosure or abuse of passwords

  Unauthorised or inaccurate modification of data – remedy need to control modification and increase detection rates by:
  – use of passwords and hardware checks to limit update functions by person/location
  – validation checks in programs to ensure updates in range
  – programme checks to establish control totals of updates
  – audit trail creation to enable tracing of any update back to source
  – division of duties to ensure effective checks and balances in operation
  – actions of audit or security group to ensure controls are relevant and suitable for risks observed and are being complied with in practice

  Interruption of service – remedies duplicate components most prone to failure and provide speedy and reliable backup services to enable services to be resumed
  – uninterruptible power supply
  – back up copies of data files
  – back up copies program files
  – specified maintenance and support contract
  – spare hardware available e.g. printer
  – adequate stores (e.g. printer cartridges, paper, diskettes)

2 (a) Windows operating environment: (meaning an operating system) – is a program or suite of programs which controls the entire operation of the computer system. It:

  (i)   Provides common code for functions needed by most programs (e.g. input/output, file access);
  (ii) Controls access to peripherals (e.g. printers);
  (iii) Supports multiprogramming (allows switching between programs whilst maintaining the integrity of individual programs, manages interrupts)
  (iv) Provides operator interface (manages communication with the human operator)

  Significance: The Windows operating system is now the standard for most PCs. This means that it is the one with which users are most familiar and means that when we recruit staff there will be reduced requirements for re-training. Also it is the environment for which most software packages have been written giving availability of most choice at least cost. The cost of all this is that Windows requires a lot of main storage or memory to operate in, a large amount of hard disk space for its residence and a relatively fast processor speed to be able to utilise its abilities to multi task or swap been functions.

(b) In-built modem – meaning: the modem is the device which turns the digital electrical signals, which are actioned within the computer system, into the analogue signals which are transmitted down a telephone line.

  Significance: This means that the computer can be connected to service providers whose information services (legal data, stock market prices, software etc) can be accessed. It also enables connection to customers and suppliers' computers either directly or via e-mail. The higher the transfer rate of the modem, the greater the capital cost. However, there will savings to be made from reduced telephone costs because of the reduction in the time actually required connected to complete transmission.

(c) CD-ROM drive – this is a backing storage device which uses compact disk technology to store data, which may be music, video or text. This data is generally embedded on the disk at manufacture and cannot normally be amended – hence the term read only memory.

Significance: In commercial applications its most obvious current benefit is in being a reliable medium for distributing and holding back up copies of key operating and application software. A CD-ROM holds more than 20 floppy disks and can load the software on to the computer and be in operation significantly faster than loading from a floppy disk.

(d) 200 Mega Hertz processor – indicates the 'clock' speed of the processor and how many instructions per second it can perform.

Significance: Although most commercial operations do not require powerful processing facilities for the arithmetic operations they tend to use Windows operating environment which require substantial processing power to manipulate their graphical interfaces and handle their switching between tasks. In addition input/output requirements in passing data over telecommunications lines to and from services such as the Internet are expensive on processing overheads. Each generation of operating and application software becomes more attractive, easier to use and more powerful – but requires faster CPU speeds, The hardware costs extra – but the pay back is in improved software and operating performance.

(e) 3 Gbyte hard disk – Meaning: the local fixed hardware disk which is used for storing data and programmes has a capacity of 3 billion characters of information.

Significance: A 3 Gigabyte hard disk does not cost three times as much to buy as a 1 Gigabyte hard disk. The extra capacity is useful storing more archive data on-line and allowing more comprehensive databases to be held without worries of data compression and coding. The extra storage is also required to cope with the overheads of storing large operating systems (such as Windows) and applications packages (such as Office) and any graphics stored (such as in desk top publishing applications).

3 **(a)** The purpose of a feasibility study is to investigate the work of the department in sufficient depth to be able to produce a report which can either:

(I) justify upgrading the current system to solve existing problems or pursue opportunities identified or
(II) to recommend that no changes should take place because they cannot be cost justified.

To undertake a feasibility study the analysts will undertake an investigation of the current system and also seek to identify its problems and requirements and ways in which it could be improved. They will be working to Terms of Reference laid down by senior management. The general techniques of fact finding used to investigate the current system are:

Interviewing – the most widely used technique. Based on following organisation charts, departmental instructions and data flows to ask the people involved in the processes of the department what operations they actually perform in practice, together with details of volumes, trends, exceptions, perceived strengths, weaknesses and opportunities for improvement. It is the qualitative information and the opportunity to build personal relationships, vital at later implementation stages, which makes interviewing such an important technique.

Questionnaires – they save time over interviewing and are particularly useful where staff are widely dispersed and are believed to be performing the same task. However, they are difficult to design and frequently suffer from low response rates. They are often a good supporting tool for interviewing rather than a replacement for it.

Observation – the viewing of staff performing the task. This can be informal, whilst interviewing or a formal technique such as activity sampling. This is best employed alongside other techniques and can help to inform or consolidate information gained from these other sources.

Record inspection – the study and analysis of the past records of the department. Can identify all the record types involved, create metrics of work volumes, spot trends and highlight exceptions. Where exceptionally large volumes are found statistical sampling techniques can be employed to keep the volume of work required in such inspection in bounds.

Previous reports – most large organisations have had previous reports produced on most departments, by internal or external audit, O & M departments or even previous IS? IT feasibility studies by internal or external consultants. Such studies are an excellent starting point for a further study.

Special purpose records – the creation by user staff of new records for the purpose of the study – e.g. to note the number of telephone calls made or received whilst undertaking some prime task. A technique to be used with caution, if staff are already overburdened, extra work will not be popular. But used carefully it can help produce metrics on claims which have previously only been anecdotal.

Combined with fact finding there will be methods of fact recording to support further analysis. Modern structured techniques frequently use fact recording techniques which are themselves part of the analytical process (e.g. data flow modelling).

(b) As a user I would see my role not merely re-active in answering questions, but proactive in ensuring that the eventual system designed would meet my needs and that of the organisation. From a selfish point of view it will be me and my colleagues who will have to operate any new system, so it is in our interest to make our views felt. From a professional point of view, we should know more about the existing system and the opportunities for successful change than any outsider.

Therefore I would seek to gather all factual details to hand – job instructions, record types, volumes, exceptions and trends and also think through all of those opportunities for improvement which are frequently noticed but are not passed on in the heat of combat.

I would also look for the opportuity to provide quality assurance on any draft report produced and to take part in any eventual user acceptance testing.

4   *Hardware requirements*

LAN with Server and 1 PC/workstation for each member of staff;
SERVER to have High Capacity Hard Disk and floppy disk –
PC/Workstation probably HD and floppy but could be limited or disabled for security reasons; minimum 15" screen with high resolution and colour for comfortable viewing; (typical suppliers IBM, Compaq, Dell, Fujitsu etc)

Printing – at least two printers for resilience; laser printer for volume work and possible ink jet for back up and colour printing; (typical suppliers Hewlett Packard)

Modem (Typical speed 32 Kbps) for access to external bureau/Internet services; (typical service provider Compuserve, America On Line)

CD-ROM drive for software distribution purposes

Tape cassette drive for data back up

Uninterruptible power supply (UPS) to enable processing to continue in spite of power surges or interruptions to power supply

Physical storage cabinets or area for computer media – e.g. paper and for safe secure storage of back up programs and data.

Software

Operating system (e.g. Windows 95 or Windows NT, Novell)

Applications – accounting package (e.g. SAGE)

Word processing/spreadsheet/database – (typical integrated package would be Microsoft Office, Lotus SmartSuite)

Internet Web browser – e.g. Netscape.

Marks

1   **(a)**   Should protect against both accidental and deliberate security threats   1
Description of risks:
- breach of confidentiality   to 3
- risk to integrity of data and erroneous modification of data   to 3
- interruption to service due to physical or software problems   to 3

  (b)   Breach of confidentiality   – identification of potential risk   1
                                  – controls – 1 mark per point   to 4

           Modification of data   – identification of potential risk   1
                                    – controls – 1 mark per point   to 4

           Interruption of service   – identification of potential risk   1
                                    – controls – 1 mark per point   to 4
                                                            25

2   **(a) (b) (c) (d) (e)**

  2 marks for the meaning of each aspect   to 10
  3 marks for the significance of each aspect   to 15
                                                            25

3   **(a)**   up to 3 marks for each method/technique
           – interviewing, questionnaires, observation, record inspection
               previous reports, special purpose reports   to 15

  (b)   role of section leader
          reactive – answering questions, participating in interviews, questionnaires   to 4
          proactive – to input views to ensure that the new system will meet the needs of the organisation   to 4
          to gather all relevant information e.g. job instructions, record types and provide quality assurance   to 2
                                                            25

4   outline the likely uses to which the system will be put   to 3
  hardware – each component – 1 mark for naming component, up to 2 marks for the description   to 12
  software – each component – 1 mark for naming component, up to 2 marks for the description   to 10
                                                            25